ANCHOR
BOOKS

FIRESIDE FABLES

Edited by

Kelly Deacon

First published in Great Britain in 2000 by
ANCHOR BOOKS
Remus House,
Coltsfoot Drive,
Woodston,
Peterborough, PE2 9JX
Telephone (01733) 898102

HB ISBN 1 85930 754 X
SB ISBN 1 85930 759 0

FOREWORD

The challenge was set within these pages - to write a story with a beginning, a middle and an end in only 50 words; and so the mini-saga was born. Lots can be said in a few words - enabling a brief exchange between reader and writer, creating a bond as characters and stories unfold between the lines.

Read on to enjoy the very best in a huge variety of stories, tales, sagas and fables, sure to demand and delight all who read *Fireside Fables.*

Kelly Deacon
Editor

CONTENTS

GOING HOME

He lay back against the warm wood,
arms outstretched.
Soon he would be home.
He closed his eyes
against the bright sun,
The worst
of the journey lay ahead
but he imagined his joy
at seeing his father again.
Then he screamed
as the first nail went in.

Tony Coyle

SHOCKING STATE OF AFFAIRS

She read the letter again, it was obvious her husband's affair had been going on for years. She wasn't angry just annoyed she'd been such a fool. Calmly she walked to the bathroom where her husband was wallowing in the bath. The electric fire came as a shock to him.

David Whitney

THE FOOD OF LOVE!

The stench in the room was nauseating.
Each breath I took caused me to retch.
He laughed as I staggered towards an open window:
Unashamed, he thrust himself towards me,
I could feel his foul breath on my neck.
I pushed him away and yelled,
'Mark, you've been eating garlic!'

Sandra Edwards

A TALE OF FORGIVENESS BY A SAD, YET LOVING WIFE

I sit by my window most days. The girl outside seems sad, so pretty.
A man has arrived to hold her hand, dry her tears.
He seems kind yet troubled. She smiles at him.
My heart aches. Take care of her, John, as you once cared for me -
dear Husband.

Margaret Walker

ON THE ROCKS

'Whiskey on the rocks,' I said to the barman. Suddenly there was a loud crash and a gaping hole appeared in the side of the ship.

'Sorry Sir,' he replied, 'no ice. However will this do?' he asked, cutting a lump off the iceberg as the Titanic sank.

Cynthia C Berry

END OF A PRETENDER

'You are not a *real* prince!' she argued.

'I am *now!*' He was getting angry and his coronet kept slipping.

'You said you were a frog. On that lily pad.'

'So?'

'Prove it!'

A little frog appeared on the pad. The princess smiled, turned into a heron and swallowed him.

Mary Cane

CAMPING OUT

In the darkness, they shivered, huddled together for warmth and protection. They heard a noise.
Footsteps.
The leaves crackled as the silent spectre approached.
Slowly the flap began to lift.
The wind rushed in.
They all screamed, fear piercing their souls.
'Hi boys, thought you might be hungry.'
'Aw, Mum!'

J Gatenby

IMPEDIMENTAL

The ceremony began. 'Dearly Beloved . . . gathered together . . .
any impediment why you may not be lawfully joined . . .'

Policemen clattered down the aisle shouting *'Stop!* He is a psychotic
killer, murdering two more 'wives' since escaping from custody.'

The bride collapsed and died . . . of shock.

'Not guilty - this time' the bridegroom smirked.

Joy Mullins

GREEN PEACE AT LAST

Aeons after man's pollution of Earth, the Eternal Optimist re-created Paradise.

A slug, mindful of sexual equality, tempted Adam with organic fruit. Enlightened, Adam warned God:

>'Pests will devastate Paradise.'

>'I know,' sighed God, exterminating man with an ozone-friendly thunderbolt.

God winked at the slug:

>'Once bitten . . .'

Val Gough

FATE

Kenji stood looking tearfully at his beloved wife and children. They had packed enough to see them through the next few weeks. The war would be over by then. The Americans were bombing Tokyo - it was too dangerous to remain. Yes, they'd be quite safe with his aunt in Hiroshima.

John O'Neill

DEAR MUM,

Am writing from the severe burns unit at the hospital.

Hope you are not still waiting for the takeaway.

The straw house was a piece of cake, but I did have problems with the wooden one.

Remind me to leave the heavy stuff to the experts.

Ingrid Gledhill

HYPOTHERMIC

'First week was the worst!' she mumbled to herself. 'Better this way!' The liquid was sweet and revitalising, combating the pain of exposure to the extreme cold.

Totally isolated, no help in sight, she knew death was near. As she slid down a wall with bottle in hand, shoppers bustled.

Perry McDaid

THE BADLANDS

An Apache, dark, lean and lethal, lurked behind a pile of boulders. The oncoming column crawled menacingly along the rutted track. With keen eye homing in on the unsuspecting enemy, the Apache rose up screaming *'Fire!'*

'Another tank destroyed,' smiled the pilot with grim satisfaction as his helicopter whirled away.

Margaret Franklin

GLITTERING PRIZES

Her eyes poured over the glittering cache.
He certainly knew how to attract a girl to his place.
'There's plenty more where this came from . . . follow me . . .'
he urged . . .
They came to an isolated house; window ajar, jewellery in view.
Suddenly, the door burst open. The jackdaws took flight empty-handed.

Diana Moore

WHOSE LIFE

'It's my life' she said, 'I'll do what I like'
she said, she experimented with drugs
'I'll take what comes,' she said, 'life is to be lived.'
For excitement she injected herself with heroin,
germs invaded her young body. 'It's my life'
she said, But was it?
Now she's dead.

Gladys C'Ailceta

OLEG THE SLAYER, OR THE PERILS OF DRINK

The King begged Oleg the Slayer - 'Kill this pestilential giant.'
'Where is your champion Lord?'
'The giant slew him.'
'I am old' said Oleg - 'but show me this giant.'

The giant laughed - 'You kill me!'
'Drink with me then' said Oleg 'before you slay me.'
They both drank and died.

Howard Gibbs, the Saxon

THE FALL OF GOD

Leaves scattered the length of the Forum.
Ruefully, the Emperor approached the huddled
Senators.
Disrespect festered. They circled like
prowling wolves to a morning feast.
Feral intent recognised, Caesar turning
at their sudden closure,
clawing the air with each momentous dagger
thrust, croaked,
'Swiftly, Gentlemen, lest conscience
make you hesitate.'

Clive W Macdonald

THE DARKER SIDE OF THE MOON

She had loved him once, until that fateful night -
Terror surfaced as hands wrapped themselves around
her neck - enjoyment etched on his face whilst evil
gripped the man. Loosening his hands, he had left her
with an unforgettable, terrifying gaze - disappearing
into the night . . .

Until the next full moon.

Nina Graham

THE END OF THE GREAT PROJECT

It was finally all over. The construction and maintenance gang had left the site and gone to the party. One of the younger workers remained, silently gazing in wonder.

The boss strolled over.

'An impressive job,' he remarked. 'What was your favourite part?'

'That's easy, the Cretaceous.'

B W Ford

DREAM TICKET

'Congratulations, Mr Jeremy Barker. You have definitely won £500,000.' Jeremy was ecstatic. He rang work, resigned and told the boss what he really thought of him. He ordered a voluptuous car and picked up leaflets on executive houses.

Then he read the letter again . . . 'if you hold the winning number . . .'

M Clifford

BONNÉ ANNIVERSAIRÉ

He saw its glowing ember,
Rising tall, on a column of wax.
He grew afraid, and began to wonder,
As eagerly their faces pressed near.

Many voices, laughing loud,
Shouting at him, to blow, and blow,
Before silently, with one last look,
He took to the candle,
And blew.

Charles Croft

BRIAN...

Through misty eyes she gazed
at his empty chair . . . his name
just audible beneath her laboured
breath.

Twelve years of unconditional
love, gone . . . wiped out by
screeching brakes on a wet
Monday morning.

He was on his way home.

Opening her trinket box she lovingly
placed his tartan flea collar.

Linda Zulaica

USELESS KNOWLEDGE

He was always envious!
Disbelief showed on his face, as he stood upon the gallows. The fact,
that he, had had to work hard (albeit in a life of crime), when Tom, only
worked one day a month. What job paid so well?
Now he knew . . .

A hangman's!

Geoffrey C Garbutt (Bristol)

UNTITLED

The street was dark, yet it was only early
With a strange sense of foreboding he approached
the large oak door,
As he pushed it open with a creak,
He jumped as a soft voice asked,
'Do you have an appointment, Sir?'
'Yes, for a cut and shave please, Mr Todd . . .'

Sally J Robinson

A WINTER'S TALE

Stealing away in the gloom of a wintry morning, he stared from the window of the coach, shedding a single tear for the wife and children left still sleeping in their beds. Who knew what uncertainties lay ahead? Eventually, the coach door swung open, 'London, Master Shakespeare' smiled the coachman.

Andrew Detheridge

There's No Fool Like An Old Fool Or One Strike And You're Out

Knives glinted in the sun. Two pensioners
glared angrily. Both swore to fight to the
death for the hand of the woman they loved.

After ten minutes posturing, they struck
simultaneously. Neither was mortally wounded
.

Sixty-year-old Maria rejected both for
'being stupid enough to fight over a woman'.

Roy Gordon

UNTITLED

The horn-helmeted warriors shoved out to sea
leaving their dead skewered to the shingle.
Arrows and tomahawks rained down on the longship
as they rowed furiously away.

'Shame we can't come back,' said Leif Ericsson,
'this place has definite possibilities.'

Chris Jenkinson

INDECISION

It's not there, of course it's there -
get a grip.
Oh God, I've lost it, *I have!*
I left it until the last minute because I
didn't know what to do about the winnings
and now the lottery ticket's out of date.
That's my trouble - indecisive:
Shall I commit suicide?

Paddy Jupp

How Could The Weak Be Eliminated?
Only By Way Of The Law Of Natural Selection

Mud clouds raining, thundering earth a battleground
Churned by snarling beasts. So close the quarry
Could sense the breath of his predators.
Blood boiling, spoiling to be spilled.
The smell of death charged the air.
The victim dropped guard, bit dust
And Madam Speaker called for order
in the House.

Patricia Thompson

A HEAD ABOVE THE REST

A tower formed out of planks, ropes
and scaffolding, with stepladders on
all levels, provided access for a
man who persevered . . . lay on his back
for many years.

Each painstaking brush stroke
created a great masterpiece.
Yet this man's skilfulness was
doubted by a powerful Holy-man.
Regardless, Michaelangelo
carried on.

Sue Gardham

ROSES

Life was easy
He knew that
He had a gift
He was going to share this gift with her
She was everything to him
Mum gave him life
She could have had had an abortion
She gave her son life
He gave her roses
On her grave
She dies
He lives.

J M Stoles

TIME FOR REGRET

Panic gripped her as she studied her swollen stomach.
After three years of marriage she and her husband were
looking forward to the birth.
The news which caused her anxiety was that her
ex-boyfriend had just died of AIDS.
Just when had he contracted the disease? she wondered.

Derek Beavis

AN APPARITION AT MIDNIGHT IN INTENSIVE CARE

Had Intensive Care saved my life?
The pain had gone.
Then I saw the Angel with a golden halo in a gown
shining white by my bed.
I was ready to go, her look of compassion had
stilled my fears.
I looked again.
My blonde nurse spoke 'Feeling better now?'

Ruth Mollon

HAWTHORN HOUSE

The house was dark. I approached, my torch illuminating the door. Unhesitatingly I unlocked, entering the dusty hall, silently standing, listening. No sound.

Something brushed my face, whispering. Panicking, running, losing my nerve and the fifty-pound bet, to stay two hours! I knew now the tales were true. Haunted!

Valerie Ansell

A Dully And Misty Landing

Eric was not pleased at all for it was very dull and misty as they made their way along the coast looking for their arranged landing place. Another look at his men rowing, told him they were getting somewhat mad, all the better for when they landed in Britain.

Keith L Powell

THE METEOR

The men of the village sat happily in the pub drinking to the future of an Elder's firstborn son; the women were indoors sewing, cooking or reading, doing womanly things.

Just one small innocent boy gazing at the stars saw the future as it hurtled relentlessly towards them . . .

Valerie McKinley

UNLUCKY FOR SOME

HMS Arethusa was on a Malta trip from Alexandria when a torpedo exploded in a fuel tank below crowded mess decks. Sixty-seven were buried at sea as the ship crawled slowly back to Alexandria. A dozen badly burned were the first ashore.

Survivors had no sleep for four days.

H Atkinson Ex-AB (RN)

INTO THE LABYRINTH - A TEST OF COURAGE

Arduous descent. The winding passageway eventually opened up into a dimly-lit cavern.

Claustrophobia, then fear. Opposite, three black entrances beckoned - the air poisoned with the stench of rotting flesh.

With sword drawn, I steadied myself and listened. Silence . . . snorting . . . then came the challenging deep muffled roar of the Minotaur.

Angus Alexander Brown

In Your Dreams

'In your dreams' she calls, to show she does not care.
'In my dreams,' he thinks, 'I'll keep you safely there.'
The Nymphet cycles carelessly to meet
Head on, the car that's coming up the street.

Patrick Davies

A QUANTUM LEAP INTO . . .

God was never a white-haired man in the sky . . .
. . . but a Life-Force Energy,
. . . a Power from within
which moves in mysterious ways, evolving
over billions of years . . . fire; earth; air; water;
minerals; vegetables, and all creatures
great and small.

Then order turned into chaos . . .
. . . the Mad Scientist arrived!

Tricia Nolan

A Sour Moment

It was nearly closing time, the scruffy man came into the shop and brandished the object across the counter. It could go off at any time. The nervous shopkeeper reached into the till for some ready cash. The yoghurt was well past its sell-by date.

T A Napper

THE DRAGON

The cave would always be his home, but he knew he had to leave,
Otherwise people would find him and slay him.
He looked one last time into his home, then flew off into the clouds, his
colourful wings flapping.
He knew that he would be happier in another place.

Melanie Jane Hickling (16)

THE SAGA OF THE WEB AND HER LIBERATION FROM SLAVERY

She was created by the military to do their bidding,
But she met the industrialist
And was seduced by his offer of freedom.
But he was fey and tried to rule her,
And she wept bitter tears.
But then came home PCs and she escaped onto the
internet, running free.

Bill Hayles

They Stood Waiting, A Man And A Woman.
It Was Dark, Very Dark Indeed.

The wind rustled the trees.
'Do you think it will be tonight?'
'It might be.'
'Will it be all lit up and noisy?'
'We will hear it long before we see it.'
'Where is everyone?'
'Fingers crossed, get ready . . .'
It could be heard now, 'See, look.'

The last bus showed its lights.

K Ainsley

THE NIGHT CHRISTMAS FELL APART

A stocking, a letter, mince pie and a glass of sherry by the bed. What's that noise - Santa?

No, it's coming through the floorboards!

Cold lino against her cheek, she listens.

Angry, muffled voices, screams, whimpers of pain?

Frightened, bewildered, the little five-year-old climbed back into bed . . .

Margi Hughes

GYPSY FAMILY

The star it twinkled overhead
and straw was scattered for a bed.
A girl so slender now did bear
a son in cool September air.

And as they tramped seeking food
soldiers pushed them rather rude.

They were then herded on a train
and would not see Berlin again.

Jean Paisley

Man Playing God

In 2003 AD Man embarked on a cloning programme. Emily is one of millions who had her genes tampered with.

Today is her 22nd birthday - she should not age beyond this year.

She has been programmed to live for 500 years during which time she will be perpetually rejuvenated.

Doreen Jones

PERFECT KNOWLEDGE

'Them's not mushrooms, Bill.'
'Do you think I don't know mushrooms
when I see them?'
'Well, I'll leave it to you.'

'We commit this body to the earth in
the sure and perfect knowledge that our
servant, Bill, shall merit eternal life.'

'Bill never would own up to being wrong.'

Frank Keetley

THE LAND BETWEEN

Downstairs was flooded. Upstairs was tinned food,
a bed and a radio.
She stared at the picture, a woodland scene. It seemed real.
She drifted off to sleep, waking in a forest. From the waiting
group assembled she heard a familiar voice.
'What took you so long?' it said.

Kathleen Mary Scatchard

VISITING THE MARAE EYES SEEMED TO WATCH ME FROM ANCESTORS' PICTURES ON THE WALLS

Remembering to take my shoes off, standing at the doorway of the ancient marae, brown-faced children watched me closely. Hours later, candlelight flickering, I'd heard tales of Maori battles and culture. After, we all said a prayer; I fell into a deep sleep listening to beautiful Maori singing.

Patricia Gray

A Holiday Affair

His lecher's eye picked out a luscious blonde, sunbathing. She could not resist his practised charms.

Their week-long sex orgy over, he swore eternal love and gave her a phoney address.

She kept what she had given him, and so will he until it makes him 'late' too early.

Cyril Mountjoy

FAITH CAN MOVE MOUNTAINS

Blind from birth, a beggar forced to earn
his crust of bread.
Following the sounds of the noisy crowd.
He cried for help from this strange
man.
'What can I do for you?'
The stranger asked.
'Lord I want to see.'
'Go,' He said, 'your faith has
Made you whole.

Sherry White

THE SNOW CREATURES

Deep in the forest lived snow creatures
Half-human, half grizzly bear
Long ago a young girl had been dragged away
The grizzly bear mated with her
She gave birth to an evil creature
its appetite was for human flesh.
Each new moon villagers gave a young
maiden in sacrifice.

Ann Hathaway

CHRISTMAS EVE

(Little Nellie stood at the prison gate
lightly clasping a small paper parcel)

Little Nellie called to Prison Governor,
'Please Sir, Mama's dead, I want to see Papa.'
Governor called No.37. Nellie handed over parcel
containing golden curl from her brother's head before he died.
Prisoner sobbed uncontrollably. Governor took scantily-clad
child home where she lived until her father was released, reformed.

Frances Gibson

CHARLIE, DEATH AND THE GUARDIAN ANGEL

Charlie's guardian angel and Death met at the gates of heaven.
'Today,' said Death, 'I am going to take Charlie.'
'Over my dead body,' replied the angel.
As Charlie made his way to work a car braked suddenly.
An angel smiled, Death cursed, and Charlie lived to see another day.

Joyce Walker

INDOMITABLE

They left their house and went into the mountains.
There they found a cave and waited.
The storm was fierce and they knew that their house would be
destroyed.
When the storm passed, they went down and began rebuilding,
Knowing that in six months' time, there would be another storm.

Connie Voss

A Ghostly Farewell

The house was old and she lived alone there
For many years - but never felt alone.
When aged, she had to move to a smaller
abode, and was sad.
On departure day, she turned to have a last
look, and saw, for a fleeting moment, the
image at the window!

Jean McDonald

THE DINNER DATE

He awaited her arrival with a mixture of hope and trepidation -
things had gone wrong in the past.
'If she does come, will I be able to hold on to her this time?' he thought.
Maurice felt rather than saw or heard her arrive - and he hurried across
his web.

Ian Cross

SHELL SHOCK

In the North Atlantic
On simulated war exercises
In the ship's ammunition magazine.
Our job
To send shells to gun turrets.
A shell got trapped in the conveyor doors.
The nozzle hitting the bulkhead
Smoke, cordite, was everywhere.
Everyone screamed.
An officer switched off the conveyor.
We were all safe.

Michael John Swain

THEY SEEK HIM HERE, THEY SEEK HIM THERE
THE PIMPERNEL IS EVERYWHERE!

(With love to my daughter Rebecca - my inspiration.)

Wooden cart wheels rumbled over cobbles - sobs - stifled screams as Madam Guillotine claimed her victim. Isobella shook violently, stumbling up crude steps, kicked by a guard.

Then, sound of hooves flying over cobbles, and *whoosh* - in a trice she was scooped up alongside the horseman to safety in England.

Mary Louise

As If

Rodin was a Norwegian warrior, and was feeling down, and very miserable, so he decided to go for a walk around the fjord, he came to a spot by the river and spotted something shining. Reaching down, he picked up a sword, inspecting it. He found it to be Oden's.

Freda Bill

STEVEN, THE RELUCTANT VIRGIN

At 8.50 Steven the reluctant virgin, joined the back of the Pox Clinic queue, along with others who faced the wall or hid beneath large hats. Steven faced out, yearning to be seen by anyone he knew. At 9.00 doors opened but Steven went home, reputation still intact. Sadly.

Ray Burton

UNDER THE SHADOW OF HIS FATHER

Orog thought of his gallant father as he sharpened his father's sword, could he ever do such brave epic feats of heroism?

Stories would be told, he would be remembered forever, Pallor crept over his face, he packed a bag, his future's fate laid in the dark of night.

K W K Garner

LAST ORDERS

Clatter of horses' hooves -
Seconds later, seven men enter.
Everyone in the bar freezes,
The landlord turns pale,
His hand shakes as he takes a lantern,
He leads the seven to the cellar
Grabbing the contraband, they leave laughing -

The Redcoats are waiting -
And so ends the landlord's fortnightly ordeal.

Thomas C Ryemarsh

HELP!

The stranger showed the landlord a photograph.

'She was here last night,' he admitted, 'asking for help with her car.'

"I'm no charity," 'I said,' "Buy a drink or get out!"

The stranger wept.

'Her death be on your conscience,' he cried. 'That's my daughter. She was murdered last night.'

Colin Winfield

GENETICALLY MODIFIED HUMANS

'It hit all the news headlines, it was this woman doctor who started developing abnormal cells - they called it Cancer back then. Yeah! Funny thing it was . . . you see, they didn't know that much about cloning then, and it didn't dawn on them that these abnormal cell growths were due to an abnormality in the cloning programme.'

Dawna-Mechelle Lewis

CAREER MOVE

'So clear at seventeen,' Tracey confided to Susan. 'Take life easy - get A levels and have really groovy social life.'

'Then a degree?'

'Or job. Fancied money - and status - police-work.'

'Didn't you plan what you've got then?' Susan checked.

Tracey laughed. 'No! Took precautions. Caught.'

'All three?'

'No,' Tracey said, 'Middle one planned.'

Robert D Shooter

Now There Is A Flag In All My Corners

Remember that boy in the corner wearing a hat with a big 'D'?

Reading or writing were not for me. That was years ago.

Look outside at my Porsche in the street. Football is my game. Using my head and feet. Life's been good for me. I still cannot read.

Frank E Trickett

A NIGHT HOUSE SITTING FOR A FRIEND'S OLD HOUSE

Sam woke up with a start and saw shadows in the corner of the room. The floorboards creaked and Julie's doll started to talk, Sam thought he would die of fright. The shadows moved towards him, he sighed, it was only Julie who thought it was a joke. He did not.

D A Fieldhouse

A STRANGE HAPPENING

The night was eerie,
The moon behind the clouds.
The path through the wood was difficult to see.
What was that in front of me -
A creature of the wild?
It turned, it was beautiful - white and light!
I gazed with fascination,
It fled and was lost.
A 'phantom' perhaps?

Olivia Wheatley

THE LADY OF INDEPENDENCE, LIVING AN IMPERSONALLY COLD UNCLUTTERED EXISTENCE, BEWARE!

Rich in health and possessions, companion paid, served
without question.
Friends, family she had none, her choice, alone emotionally sterile.
Luxurious house, garden with pool, not shared, no joyous venue.
Man of violence, intent to rob, took her life without remorse.
Constant companion inherited the unused pile.
Wisely constants guile.

Evelyn Poppy Sawyer

TICK . . . TICK

My whole life is just a repetition,
This is how I was made.
I just go round and round in one big circle,
Going absolutely nowhere.
I can't make any decisions, I just continuously go . . .
Tick . . . tick . . . tick . . . tick . . . tick . . . tick

Zoe Puttock

2000

It's still 1999 as we gazed out into the sky, waiting, for the moment to arrive. It's 12 o'clock on the dot. Big Ben chimes ding, dong, dong. Fireworks everywhere. People celebrating here and there. Shouting it's the year 2000. A new year of life.

Candice Asher (11)

VOLCANO SURPRISE

I stood back and watched it,
Thick orange blobs warming up within the bright lighted background.
It started to rise, and my eyes were drawn towards it.
The lava lamp looked beautiful in the middle of the room.

Naaila Mohammed (13)

OUIJA BOARD

The glass moved slowly, methodically across the board.
They knew the force behind the movement was evil.
The feeling lingered in the air like petrol smoke.
Someone screamed.
Contact with the spirit had been broken.
The glass exploded in the candlelight.
Crystal shards rained down deafeningly like icy hailstones.

Gina Brewis (15)

DESOLATION . . . CONSOLATION . . . RECONCILIATION

('Weep with those who weep' St Paul to Romans Ch 12)

A young boy said to his dad:
'My pal, Peter, was very unhappy today, because his little dog died
yesterday - but I consoled him when he cried'
'Good lad! Did you tell your little friend to be brave and stop crying?'
'No Dad! I only helped by crying with him.'

Leonard Jones

Calling Me Home

Sitting alone with my memories, the creak of the rocker made me turn.
The room turned icy cold and gently rocking sat a young soldier from a
war long gone. Through a mist stood a young girl, her hand on his
shoulder, I knew their faces, especially my own.

Eileen Carter

Sounds In The Attic

It was dark outside, night had fallen as Yasmin tucked herself under the blankets, she heard a knocking then scratching sound coming from the attic.

What was it? The sounds got louder and frightening and suddenly it seemed like hell was let loose upstairs, then silence, everything went quiet, why?

Beryl Sylvia Rusmanis

BAD JUDGEMENT

Once, three wise men travelled miles to reach an old king -
using the stars as navigational aids:
spreading rumours that a pretender to the throne had been born.

Cleverly, the king talked them into returning, when the boy was located.
Once found, he'd be killed and no one would ever know!

Pat Derbyshire

THE FRIGHT OF MY LIFE

I felt a cold chill run down my spine as the shadow moved closer towards me. My heart pounded loudly. I tried to run but my legs wouldn't budge. Then, I felt a cold, clammy hand on my shoulder.

'Happy Hallowe'en!' yelled my little sister. 'Do you like my costume?'

Nicola Kirby (11)

CIRCLE OF CIRCUMSTANCE

Tom, thirteen, petrified of heights,
and bullied at school, now, on the annual school trip,
he was being forced to ride the Big Wheel.
He was apprehensive,
twice it had stuck,
his feelings were sheer terror,
it turned, it stopped,
in blind panic, he lifted the safety bar,
and jumped.

Jacqueline Claire Davies

A Danish Fable

Sailing in their distinct long ships, Vikings invaded the land.
Ferocious pirates in looks and behaviour. Robbing and destroying
English churches, villages and monasteries.
Eventually settling down in the north and east of England.
Promising 'Alfred the Great' they would keep the peace.
But the peace pact did not last!

R E Humphrey

THE GREAT ESCAPE

The vast sea stretched before them, mountains reared up either side as their enemy bore down from the rear.

'Why lead us so many miles, only to die here?' the people asked their leader.

It was then Moses turned, faced the water then raised his hands and Staff to heaven.

Ron Beaton

NEGATIVE

My dream had been vivid.
The characters appearing stayed
With me on awakening.
I knew not the place they
Took me to. I knew not
The characters.
What was this dream?
Why has it disturbed me so?
Why can't I remember it now?
I'll never know.

Barbara Sherlow

HEADLINE - DEATH STALKS A NORTHERN TOWN

His was a gentle, bearded figure, well loved,
avuncular, kind. He strode about his northern
town, healing the sick and bringing peace to
hundreds - strangely, all females, past sell-by
date. They smiled and thanked him as he watched
them sail across the waters of Lethe.

Well-named, our Doctor Shipman.

Eileen M Lodge

REFLECTION OF REALITY

Calm waters, 'Cast off', cruising smoothly,
sudden pitch, wind bellowed, tossed,
rocked, heaved, sighed.
Cascading waves, above us,
storm force nine.
Sinking, swelling, bows soaring above us,
banging, crashing, wind, screaming, raging.
Elements exchanging, blow after blow.
Determination, must survive . . .
Someone, somewhere, called 'land',
Heads raised, eyes focused,
hope ascended . . .

Lorna Tippett

THE UNSEEN HAND AND VOICE WERE WORTH LISTENING TO, DID THEY SAVE MY BABY'S LIFE?

My baby was desperately ill, no hope I was told, but I knew different
when a hand on my shoulder and a voice spoke to me
'You give her will to live'
Yes, I prayed. Five weeks later I took her home. I'd listened, I'd
obeyed, my faith won through.

Olive Wright

UNTITLED

I broke my lover's heart, when I chose the three years, world travel adventure, instead of her. Now I'm the heartbroken one. I love her, and want marriage, but, too late. She has a ring on her finger - not mine - and a baby in a pram . . . My big mistake . . .

Flora Passant

It's True - I Saw It From My Window

1963 - snow deep on the ground, lying there for weeks - a space beneath the cedar tree to feed the birds. They came in their dozens. The cats, domestic and feral, watched from a distance: no hunt, no hassle. Creatures can be kinder than man.

Martha Fear

THE GIRL

There she was. Church (what a place to meet her) no chance to talk, a glance then next time 'Friday evening, okay?' Holding hands, making plans, kissing lips, heart pounding. Can I marry your daughter please? Away to college (adding an edge to the happiness), then the end, heart breaks.

John D Riddett

THE CREATION

With his chisel and small brush
He got to work on his sculpture
When he had finished, he stood
back and looked at it.

It walked towards him and strangled
him into dust.

The creation picked up the chisel and
brush. And walked to the untouched
slab of granite.

David Rosser

EXAM RESULTS

During breakfast it fell through the box. We all rushed to get it 'Oh no, exam results!'
Everyone expectant to see straight As
E, E, E . . . 'Eh . . . at least they're straight.'
'Up to your room.'
I felt the envelope still in my hand, turned it over and '*Joke! Your friend Sonia*'.

Mst Shahmima Khanom (19)

HOPS AND 'WINE'!

'Can I go out to play Mum?' Grip released, hopscotch jumping on safe
pavement. A stumble interrupts the laughter. Speeding monster. *Impact!*
She is gone! *But wait!* Paramedic shows relief. She is returned to us.
'There *is* a God - first in all things - content to wait. Second chance!'

John L Wright

O MY SOUL I GAVE YOU BACK FREEDOM

He was disillusioned with life.
Went into isolation. Conversed with his soul. Realised
God was dead, that man-made God. Turned to the will instead.
A free . . . spirit! Found out all about self-control. Self-creation.
And the best in man. Love is your destiny, he said.
He died insane.

Claire-Lyse Sylvester

THE HAPPIEST DAYS OF YOUR LIFE

Slowly he trudged to school. Homework, spellings, maths. Undone, unlearnt, misunderstood. He longed for his mother and his soft furred bear. Also to school went Miss, knowing she must somehow cope with homework, spellings, maths. Undone, unlearnt, misunderstood. But, wait. She is a mother. Her bear has long grown up.

Bill Cottle

TRAPPED!

A woman in Italy sadly died,
After her death, she came back as a spirit,
She indicated to her family,
That she had mistakenly taken for dead,
Whilst in a coma.

The body was exhumed,
The corpse was lying twisted,
Bruised, and fingernails torn,
From clawing at the coffin.

Trapped.

Sylvia Khan

THE TORTURE CHAMBER

I could hear the screams of pain from inside the room,
It was my turn next to enter the torture chamber,
The people in white coats forced me onto the large chair.
I was paralysed with fear . . .
'Open wide' said the man sat next to me.
I hate the dentist.

Emma Luke (15)

A Demon! Or Is It . . .

'Ouch,' I yelped, as he hit me hard.
But he didn't stop.
What had I done to anger him?
His eyes were lit like coals burning brightly in ebony sky.
It had suddenly hit me, I had sat on his tail.
'Okay, okay, I'll go,' I said to my cat.

Nadine Chatergon (13)

SHOWTIME!

The tension builds, waiting in the shadows of the wings. All the months of preparation for this moment, this moment that is finally here. Will I be good enough or will I fail? It's time to find out. The music starts, the curtains lift . . . it's showtime!

Amy Collins (12)

SILENCE

Take away what I have dreamt
Now I've entered this
Silence
Bang
The bomb erupted
Millions of people
Screaming yelling too
I scream
My family, my dreams
Now I've gone away
Heaven is a wonderful place

Kimberley Portas (15)

THE RED SEA

Constant noise from guns and shells,
And the groans of dying men.
Once this field was a red sea, of blood.
Now the guns are silenced,
But the field remains red.
Now the only sound,
Is the wind,
Blowing through petals.
And the swaying poppies,
Are the red sea.

Jordan Steer

INVASION

They came without warning hidden by the dark,
In that burning night my green and blue world died,
The night ended and against all disbelief the sun rose again,
We survivors emerged into the pale light,
To face our new masters,
The tyrants who called themselves humans.

Katy Brown

RESTORATION

She was desperate.
She had spent all her money, yearning to be healed.
He walked in the crowd, which pressed hard around Him.
She touched His cloak at last!
Healing, freedom, joy!
He knew all about her suffering
And she gave thanks to her Saviour.

Judith Thomas

A Vision Heard

He knew the law was on his side. He had to stamp out this new sect sweeping the land. Suddenly brilliant light so dazzled him he couldn't see, but he heard this wonderful, emotional voice asking him why. Even though he was blinded, Paul could at last see the way.

Jennifer Stella Smeed

Look At It Go

Look, look, look at it go.
Its wings are strong
Stronger than anything in the world.
It's flying in and out
Those fluffy white clouds.
Look, look, look at that seagull go.

Mary Duffy

A KIND OF BLINDNESS

She walked her dog, as usual, through the park. Stepping in something, she cursed the other dogs. The afternoon brought children after school. Somebody's shoes, some little hands were fouled. Secretly, a tiny egg found its new host. 'Toxicara?' 'Not my dog' she said, hurrying blindly past the waiting mothers.

Ivor F Standen

ON A COLD WINTER'S NIGHT

Outside the Maypole Inn in the village of Chigwell, a stagecoach draws up and out steps the ghost of Charles Dickens.

He espies the Landlord bound and fastened to a chair being released by the Parish Clerk whilst fire is raging.

Returning to the stagecoach, he disappears into the night.

Barbara Fosh

RELIEF

Our ship was about to leave Suez.
'Stop!' I was on the wharf.
'Madam, where is your pass?'
'Gone!'
'You cannot leave!' I was hustled by three Arabs.
Would they take me to a harem?
I took all my money and gave it. They waived me on.

Nola B Small

DAWN RAID

Nothing would go wrong. Practice runs had been perfect. No hiccups.
They all knew what had to be done. They would soon be rid of him.
Dawn came. At a call from their leader they took off. Whistling,
screaming, screeching they attacked. Retreated. Looked back. They had
failed again.

C MacIntyre

SEA STORM

Splash! Went the waves as they crashed upon the deck. The hole was large, the water gushed in. As the captain cried he gave the order, 'Abandon ship.' The lifeboats were despatched as the waves crashed down, upon a deck awash with water, it sweeps its captain out to sea.

Andrew Newson (15)

UNTITLED

Suzy was gazing into her dream boy's eyes. Then she turned around and fell into a trolly, bang! She turned and fell to the ground. When she got up she saw her dream boy had seen everything and was laughing at her. She never went shopping for her mum again.

Rebecca Davies

NEW YEAR'S EVE

As the clock chimed the children's eyes gazed in wonderment at the amazing spectacle of the heavens ablaze with fantastic fireworks.

They didn't fully realise what all the fuss was about, but they would remember for the rest of their lives everybody going balmy when the clock stopped chiming twelve.

M Wood

THE SHOP THAT HELD A MILLION DREAMS

The shop was deserted, dusty, sad and chilled. The door creaked alarmingly as she entered. She closed her eyes tightly and then gazed around. Lisle stockings packed in boxes, hats on composite heads, Aunt Lil standing there . . . Memories of another era . . . inside was then - both real - outside was today . . . joined.

Joan Richardson

THE HUNTER'S TALE

The sun had risen, his children were hungry. Ug headed for the
watering hole. The herd, having slaked its thirst, grazed the open plain.
Ug's children went hungry. The following daybreak Ug waited at the
plain's edge by the path leading from the lake. That day his children
were fed.

Ray Ryan

Millennium Death Throes

Death row.
Convict sleeps in cell.
Echoing footsteps.
The end has come.
Past lives, recorded events
Sweep across memory's page.

Life born in love, came youthful days.
Experience through to darkening times,
To disaster.
Knife thrust, raw agony, life's end.
And now a thousand years
Have closed, convulsed with pain.

Pettr Manson-Herrod

KIKI AND THE LEPRIS

Kiki was found in the woods as a baby of six months. His parents had perished in a car crash. Jaffu was the king of the Lepris. As his followers gathered around the human child, Kuffi asked what they should do with this child. Jaffu said 'We shall adopt him.'

M Coleman

Ieaun Surprise

Dark frosty night, Ieaun Jones, Welsh farmer with his sheepdog Bob, walking over Penrhys mountain looking for his four lost sheep. Ieaun could see his sheep stuck in the cleft of the rock, Bob barking squeezed through the rock, Ieaun followed, so surprised, he found four newly born lambs.

Christine Shurey

BOY JO

A boy named Jo went up a mountain and found an old house. He decided to go in, so he went in. He was looking for a lost football in the house, he went upstairs and there was the lost football. He took it and went back home safe.

Catherine Shurey (8)

FIXATION?

He travels at 200mph, his bid is to increase his social standing, man and machine in total harmony, with a chance to increase the team's financial handling.

If he qualifies for the grid, his efforts are partly done, described as one of man's best sport, the ever popular Formula One.

John P Evans

TOO HIGH

Flying high I saw the curve of the horizon and was caught by the majesty, the peace, the freedom of the empty air; but not for long I saw my fuel was low and turned for home too late. I parachuted, the earth rushed towards me. I landed.

Tom Hern

WASTELAND

I eat my breakfast alone,
thinking of you and wondering
where you are.

My boiled egg is hard again.
I never could cook eggs as
well as you. Without you my
breakfast is bland and bleak.

I do the washing up without
your help, hoping that you
will soon return.

Kate McDonnell

WHAT A SHOCK!

Audrey had entered the bedroom to find her mother's lifeless body. Realising that the sound she had heard had been a shot, she crossed to the phone and dialled '999'.

'Audrey, half past seven, time to get up,' her mother's voice came up the stairs. Thankfully, she woke from her nightmare.

Joyce M Turner

PAUL AGED 17

Paul was independent, happy and caring. He loved playing football. Suddenly Paul became withdrawn and irritable. His mother Judy thought it was teenage hormones, until she found a white powder. It was heroin. Judy was distraught but advice before confronting Paul. Together they tackled his drugs problem.

Danielle Gallagher

TRIUMPHANT

For years, he had written
Poetry, stories, articles
None were ever published
Slowly his ideas, enthusiasm
For it all, were waning
Rejection slips, excuses from publishers
He had had them all
Then, it happened, acceptance
His joy was overwhelming
Frustration all forgotten
It had been worthwhile.

GIG

THE 1905 NO BELL PRIZE

1905, the year fat Jack Foster became the new Town Crier.

Elated and eager voiced, 'donned his regalia' stood in the town, legs apart. Raised his heavy bell high then fell 'splosh' into a horse trough.

Stuck fast, he gurgled his message.

When retiring received wooden bell handle as a momento.

Roger Foster

MOUNTAIN TOP

A seamstress appeared with mist in her lap to embroider the sky and whisk her candyfloss round our small flames. Treacherous her embrace, but bolder our coldness. We did not take from her sweetness and refrained from temptation, a mirage at peak time.

Marylène Walker

My Natural World Of Living Peace
(Scandinavia in the Middle Ages)

You are my tree, I live in your centre, your wood surrounds me in warmth, keeping me safe, I call you 'my tree of life', your colours in the fire are my rainbow, I toast my bread, dream dreams, see pictures in my mind.

The howling wind is strength, serenity.

Elizabeth Cowley-Guscott

CRUSADES

The year 1095. March said Pope Urban 11 at the Council of Clermont. March in aid of eastern brethren. The Holy City of Jerusalem being the prize. Mounted warriors from all classes and backgrounds ransacked villages and killed the people. This they called Christianity!

Ann

WHO KNOWS WHAT LURKS AT THE EDGE OF REALITY?

It was too dark to see.

That didn't stop him knowing it was there, watching, waiting for the right moment to pounce, to sink its razor sharp teeth into his soft flesh.

He stopped!

He felt the breath on his face, smelt the putrefying odour of death.

Then he woke.

Tony Hucks

SAGA STORY

Henry Dunant was a business man,
Who wasn't the war's greatest fan.

He didn't like how the wounded laid,
So he gave them first aid.

Henry Dunant, he's the boss,
Because he founded the Red Cross.

Lindsey Roberts (9)

GOODBYE TO MARY, HELLO TO LOVE

Dan sat on his haunches
He watched Mary disappear from view.
Ten years of togetherness, a long time
Now it was over.
The sadness will pass, he will survive
Just as he did when he broke his leg
He rose and walked towards the road
Sally was waiting for him.

Don Friar

THE TALE OF DOUGLAS

I know a 3 legged friendly tabby kitten called Douglas.
He lives at PACT animal sanctuary.
He introduces himself by climbing up your leg.
Born a Siamese triplet. He was 3 days old when separated.
The weakest, he was the only survivor. His hind leg was amputated.
But he's lively!

Kirsty Hinde (10)

A FLEETING ROMANCE

They had been acquaintances for years, often meeting in the company of others.

At the bookshop, reaching out, she felt a hand tenderly caress hers. Lasting a second, no more.

Hurriedly he made his choice, paid and left. She went home perplexed.

S Mullinger

HAS MAN'S MIND EVOLVED SO MUCH - HE CAN ESCAPE THE BONDS OF FLESH?

Scientific astronauts, masters of telepathy, were blasted off
To Zargid, the most solid planet in the universe - there they were pulled
By a superlative power into its black hole, telepathic messages were
Received back on earth saying:

Calling earth - mission achieved -
Arrived in universe two -
(Deep thought) telepathic contact only.

Flo Emmons

ELECTRIC SHOCK

With clammy hands, parched mouth, Joan surveyed the carnage before her. Swiftly the glinting steel blade of the cleaver struck, spattering the walls with blood.

Fleeing in horror Joan heard a voice boom 'Can I help?'
'No,' she screamed, 'I only came in to read the meter, I'm a strict vegetarian.'

Barbara Sowden

HOME BIRTHS WERE MORE NUMEROUS IN YEARS PAST

In swirling wraith-like mist, movements, snorts behind hedges dark, young midwife bicycled to rural cottage.

Voice heard from signalbox near, 'I'll pump water, light fire.'

Baby becoming future nurse, was bridesmaid for midwife's daughter and signalman's son at their wedding.

Their daughter also became follower of 'Lady of the Lamp'.

Ivy Lott

A Changed Man

The family went into a cafe, then John said, 'Dad, someone's at our car.' Father rushed out, and grabbed a man's hand, who said his wife was ill, he needed food!

He was told of Jesus, gave an address from an old envelope, was visited, helped, and became a Christian!

Lilian M Loftus

THE WATERFALL OF LIFE

I once lived beside a waterfall in a tiny but beautiful village in the west of Ireland. A quite man sits on his chair beside the waterfall. A rose from the gardens embraces them, I have deep conversations with this waterfall which is my *soul* . . .

Rita Cleary

ODOUR OF GARLIC

Raspo Icliffe, a Brit in Paris climbed up to Montmartre. Hot in long herringbone coat and shabby beret. A mysterious character in a world of cafes, night-clubs and fast cars. Who was he? Many had the answer but none knew. Like the odour of garlic he just lingered.

Clive Cornwall

PLANE CRASH - ENGINE FAULT ON THIRD

I heard the news 'Plane crash in sea on way to Madrid 10:30 this morning.' Oh no, that's the flight Mum was meant to be on. The phone suddenly rang, it's the hospital to say that Mum's fine, thank God for that.

Paul Turner (13)

FIRE

Swirling patterns of dancing demons
reds, oranges and leaping light
chasing, trapping, catching creatures,
torturing to their heart's delight,
feeding with their burning weapon
but then the hero comes along,
winning the battle with its cold feeling
but leaving the demons' destructive song.

Lucy Harris (12)

UNTITLED

He was standing alone. Who was he? Why was he here.
She was standing alone. Who was she? Why was she here?
They were standing together. Two lone figures, draining the lives
                                                    of the living.

Gemma Brown (15)

SAILING ON THE CHARON OF STYX WITH CAPTAIN TED FALCON-BARKER

From Bonne Anse, France, to West Palm Beach, Florida
Sailing on a thirty foot sloop, 'Charon of Styx', could anything
be horrider?
Nineteen eighty and over the waves: from France to Portugal;
Madeira to Tenerife
Then across the Atlantic, forty-two days, fetching up in the Bahamas
on a reef.

Joy Sheridan

THE CASTLE

The castle stood high, with its towering pinnacles. All seemed normal, until the enemy arrived. Armed with guns they approached my territory.

The intensity of the tide roared in the moat.

They descended and fired the gun. *Splash!* A jet of water hit me. 'Get off my sandcastle!' I yelled.

Natalie Dybisz (13)

A WEED-FILLED BATTLEFIELD

Something squeezed my left shoulder. I could estimate who it was. I knew by the end of this day I'd be pushing up weeds. I slowly rotated, my assumption proven correct. I wouldn't go without a fight but I lost. I had to weed the garden after all.

Catherine Moorhead (13)

DARKNESS AND LIGHT

It was dark, listen, smashing glass. Someone calling for help. Mother unable to cope was taken away. The children were taken in next door. In the cold dawn light they awaited their fate. A children's home, months of being unloved. Father home from war and Mother well again. Happiness, home.

Marian Andrews

£90 A CUP

In the waiting room I took a coffee from the machine. There was no charge.

The consultant examined me, explaining the plastic surgery available. Written details and price lists would be forwarded.

Later I gasped at the prohibitive cost of face-lifting. The enclosed bill for that consultation alone was £90!

Patricia Wroe

THE SCHOOL TRIP

I was on a school trip and found a bottle, I opened it. Then I saw a genie, she said I had three wishes. My first wish was to win the lottery. My second wish to make the world a better place. Third one to let the genie go.

Amy Grant (12)

DAYDREAM

As she looked into the crowd with anticipation
After what can only be described as a songbird's cry
A chorus of applause surrounded her
Then as the spotlight shone in her eyes
She saw what was actually a room full of empty chairs
And saw that she was all alone.

Alene Buckle (13)

BATTLE TO THE DEATH

I was set for a battle to the death
With my sworn enemy
He longed for revenge
Our swords clashed from mighty blows
But to my surprise he ran his sword straight through me
I could see the bloody wound
Then I realised that I was
Playing my computer.

Stephen Berry (12)

UNTITLED

Faster and faster I ran as I pulled further and further away from that house. The vision of the boy in the mirror, tears rolling down his face, writing 'help' on the mirror. Suddenly I heard a voice saying 'Mark, wake up.' It was Mum, then I realised I was only dreaming.

Mark Ramshaw (11)

WASTED TIME

I stood up, as I was next in line.
'Here are your belongings for the next two years,'
A hard-faced woman shouted.
I was taken to a cell, already occupied by two others.
'Home sweet home' called the warden with a smug grin on her face.
The door slammed!

Barbara Coombes

GRANDAD

Danger! The old man grinned and held the knife threateningly above his head. The boy's eyes widened in horror as he noticed the putrid, red blood dripping from it.

The knife had been lowered, but the man's evil eyes were only inches away from his.
'Like some cranberry pie, grandson?'

Chloé Harmsworth (14)

HOLIDAY IN FRANCE!

One day, I was picking up rubbish and put some in the bin. The French bin was metal and came down on my thumb, we washed it. And then the ambulance came and took me to hospital. I had stitches in and then I was okay.

Luke Cardwell (11)

BARNEY THE POLAR BEAR

Once upon a time there lived a polar bear named Barney. He was big and muscular and loved to eat fish.

One wintry, cold morning, Barney went to get his breakfast, fish, a smelly fish. He took it back to his den to eat and have a nap.

Scott Bartlett (10)

LIFT OFF

5 - 4 - 3 - 2 - 1 lift off. Spacecraft 9 Future zoomed up. To the crew's surprise the engine stopped. 'Hang-glide down to the field by the technology cubicle,' cried Captain Clefairy. The order rang through the craft. 'To the main door' hollered the captain. Down they glided, safely, happy.

Melissa Sharpe (9)

WHAT WE EAT IN NEW GUINEA

I stand up; in front of me, magically appears a huge warrior, wearing a frown and a blow-pipe. Suddenly, twittering in the canopy, I see the object of our journey. I point 'Micropsitta Bruijnii!' He looks, smiles, lifts blow-pipe, 'No! - oh -' he's not aiming at the tiny parrots . . .

S Thomson

JUST VANISHING AWAY

Here I lie just dreaming away,
It's like heaven not like hell,
I see a shadow in the distance,
I take steps closer and closer,
Until suddenly there was a crash,
My dreams and my thoughts
Slowly vanish away.

Then I noticed it was . . .

Craig Isabel

THE INJECTION

The ogre's deadly spear loomed over me, ready to plunge into my arm.
Poison was dripping from the blade, and the ogre was trying to
convince me it was friendly. It told me that it wouldn't hurt if I kept
still, I knew better. I bolted. The spear came down. I was alive.

Claire Field (11)

THE CRAB THAT CROSSED THREE CONTINENTS

Thirty years entombed. Once, you inhabited a shell oceans away. Its beauty drew my hand to possess it. Delight on rediscovering it, cotton-wool wrapped in my Australian trunk, soon turned to grief when your orange claw dropped out. I prized your body free and buried it under my honeysuckle.

Dee Uprichard

THE INTERVIEW

Tension mounts,
As I get ready to go,
One last check in the mirror,
I step into the office,
My name is called,
Afterwards I walk home disheartened,
The phone rings, should I answer?
Gingerly, I pick up the receiver,
'Yes?'
'Miss Gibbons, you have the job.'

Michelle Ellis

Love At First Sight

He just happened to turn as she walked into the room. He would often think of fate, but this feeling was even more powerful than the images he had.

He knew nothing about this girl as she walked longingly towards him, but he knew that he was falling in love.

Paul Rowlands

THE WEDDING GHOSTS

The sun shone as we approached the church. The figure of a bride stood by the closed door. Footsteps behind made us turn to see the groom following us.

We turned back, the bride had vanished, so had the groom. They were killed on their wedding day, my friend said.

J V Ford

THE STORM OF LIFE

Wind howled and rain fell on the small farmhouse with the thatched roof. A woman was heard to cry out. The wind intensified. Suddenly the little home lost half its thatch, rain and wind poured in.

The woman smiled, in that moment, her baby girl was born - it was me.

Sarah Binstead

THE PACIFIST

The train sauntered through the South African veldt in darkness.
The South African complained,
'Get this Kaffir out of here!'
The conductor evicted the Cambridge-trained barrister from the first-class compartment.
This injustice based surely on melanin content was the catalyst for Satya Graha, but Gandhi knew better.

Robin Halder

SUBMISSIONS INVITED

MINI SAGA INFORMATION

We hope you have enjoyed reading this book and that you will continue to enjoy it in the coming years.

If you would like more details on *Mini Saga* publications or on how to send in entries then drop us a line or give us a call and we'll be happy to send you a free information pack.

Mark your envelope
Mini Saga Information
And send to:
Anchor Books
Forward Press Ltd
Remus House,
Coltsfoot Drive
Woodston,
Peterborough,
PE2 9JX

Tel: 01733 898102
Fax: 01733 313524